# • Contents •

These Practice Tests for Key Stage 1 English assess silent reading, spelling and handwriting using material from *Oxford Reading Tree*, the most widely used series of reading books in primary schools.

The tests have been designed for three specific purposes:
- to help children gain experience of the kind of questions contained in written tests such as the Key Stage 1 tests (England and Wales) and similar tests in Scotland, Northern Ireland and the Irish Republic
- to practise the parts of the Key Stage 1 tests where practice really benefits children
- to help you to assess a child's skills in reading, spelling and handwriting

These tests are most appropriate for children from six to eight years old with reading abilities around or above the level of an average seven year old.

We have concentrated on the written tests: reading comprehension, spelling and handwriting. However, the national assessment process also includes teacher-administered tasks, such as reading aloud and writing.

## The Key Stage 1 tasks and tests

### 1. Reading aloud
Children choose a story book from several which have been selected by their teacher from a nationally approved list of books. The teacher will ask questions like, *Do you like the cover?* or *Have you read any other books like this one?* The teacher will then ask the child to read the book, but will give help to those who are still at Level 1. In each book there are a few pages which the child may be asked to read on their own, to provide an assessment at Level 2. As the child reads, the teacher records errors and looks for evidence that the child is using some or all of these strategies:

### At Level 1:
    recognising words
    phonics (sounding out)
    keeping an overall sense of the passage
    taking notice of punctuation

    responding to what is being read (by comments, or amusement)
    following the text (by pointing or turning the page at the right time)

### At Level 2:
    reading independently and accurately
    reading with pace, fluency and expression
    using a variety of reading strategies in combination
    confirming meaning (by re-reading or looking ahead)

Assessing a child reading aloud is a complex and skilled process. Teachers use their professional skills and experience to determine the precise level of reading skill at Levels 1 and 2. The best way for parents to help children do well in this part of the test is by reading to and with them regularly and discussing the cover of the book (*What does it show?*), the title (*What do we expect the story to be about?*) the pictures (*What sort of person do you think this is?*) and the whole story (*Did you like it? What did you like best about it? Did you think it would end like that?*).

### 2. Reading comprehension
If a child's reading out loud shows that he or she is above Level 1, then the child will do a written test of reading comprehension, testing their ability to read and understand passages of greater difficulty and of different types of text (fiction, non-fiction). The full range of comprehension activities and the range of ways ways in which children record answers are covered in these tests.

In the Key Stage 1 tests, Level 2 is assessed by a single booklet with answers on the page; Level 3 has a separate reading booklet and answer booklet.

### 3. Writing
The writing task at Key Stage 1 is very 'open-ended' and assessment is based on a piece of writing which children do in the context of class discussion, led by the teacher, about a topic which may be based on materials which children have used in the formal reading assessment or on 'ideas arising from the planned work of the class'. The process of

# Practice Tests
## for Key Stage 1

# ENGLISH

John Aldridge and Keith Gaines

Oxford University Press

*Acknowledgements*
Many thanks to the editorial team at
Aldridge Press: Charlotte Rolfe, Maregold
Ofei, Sheila Dampney, Jocelyne and
David.

The publisher acknowledges the following
for the use of copyright material:

The text for 'The giant baby', 'A real
giant?', and 'Stories about giants' adapted
from *The school play*, and 'Castles' adapted
from *The playroom* both by Adam Coleman
in *Oxford Reading Tree* published by Oxford
University Press, 1992. The poem 'Time
slip' is taken from 'Castle Poems' compiled
by John Foster in *Oxford Reading Tree*,
1992.

Photographs: © English Heritage, p21;
Comstock, Inc. – John Hodder, p19; Keith
Gaines Archives, pp18, 42, 43; Aldridge
Press.

Oxford University Press, Great Clarendon Street,
Oxford OX2 6DP

Oxford New York
Athens Auckland Bangkok Bogotá Buenos Aires
Calcutta Cape Town Chennai Dar es Salaam
Delhi Florence Hong Kong Istanbul Karachi
Kuala Lumpur Madrid Melbourne Mexico City
Mumbai Nairobi Paris São Paulo Singapore
Taipei Tokyo Toronto Warsaw

and associated companies in Berlin Ibadan

*Oxford* is a trade mark of Oxford University Press

© John Aldridge and Keith Gaines 1997
First published 1997
Reprinted 1998 (twice)

ISBN 0 19 838201 4

Designed by Geoffrey Wadsley
Illustrations by Julia Osorno, Jane Gedye,
Steve Smith
Packaged by Aldridge Press

Printed in Hong Kong

assessing writing is one which demands professional training, and is not a process which parents can easily help carry out.

### 4. Handwriting
Handwriting, as a specific skill, is something that can be usefully practised at school and at home, and a handwriting passage and guide to assessment are included in this book.

### 5. Spelling
Spelling is assessed by teachers in children's written work and also by tests which require children to write words cued by pictures and to write words within a dictated passage. All the forms of formal spelling assessment are covered in these tests.

## How to use these tests

The tests are intended to give children practice in the written parts of the Key Stage 1 tests, but their administration need not be formal. Children should not be pressured by an atmosphere of 'being tested', but you are likely to learn more about the child's true levels of attainment in reading and spelling skills if you avoid discussing the answers during the test itself.

There are ten tests in all. Five sections test different kinds of reading, there are four spelling tests and there is one short handwriting test. Flexibility is built into these tests, but it is recommended that the child begins at Reading Test 1 and works through the tests in order. You should spread the tests over several sessions. At the very least a short break should be allowed between each test.

## Setting up the test

The child needs a flat surface (such as a table) to work on, and a pen or pencil. Make sure the room is quiet and there are as few distractions as possible. The test should be informal and no part of the tests needs to be timed, although you may find it useful to record the start and finish times of the test. Boxes are provided for this at the top of each test. Each section requires a brief introduction but no specific wording is needed, other than a precise identification of the words to be spelled in the spelling tests. If a test is clearly too hard, allow the child to leave it uncompleted.

The tests are split into two tiers, so that you can mark *Levels 2-3: Giants* before the child begins *Levels 3-4: Castles*. If the questions in *Giants* are clearly within the child's abilities, you can leave marking until all the tests have been completed.

However, if you are unsure as to whether the child should go on to the more difficult questions in *Castles*, you can check their progress on *Giants*. If the child scores less than 15 on the three *Giants* reading tests, he or she will probably find *Levels 3-4: Castles* stressful and frustrating and you are advised not to ask the child to attempt it, although you can of course return to these tests at a later date.

## Notes for each test

**Reading Test 1:** The giant baby
(fiction: multiple choice questions and short written answers)

This activity requires the child to read a whole question and choose the most appropriate answer. When the child has read the first part of the story on page 7, explain that you want him or her to answer these questions either by ringing the word or phrase which best answers the question, or by writing a short answer. Use the example question (*What was the giant called?*) to show the child how to record their answers. Then ask the child to look at the practice question (*Which country did Finn live in?*) and to write in the answer. Tell the child to read to the end of the story (page 15) and to try to answer all the questions.

**Reading Test 2:** A real giant?
(non-fiction: true / false answers)

These questions, in a simple true/false format, require a deeper and more inferential understanding of the text and pictures. Explain, if necessary, what true and false mean and show the child how to tick the right box, using the example question. Ask the child to read the next three pages (16 to 18) about *A real giant?*, and to answer the questions at the bottom of each page.

**Reading Test 3:** Stories about giants
(non-fiction and fiction: multiple choice, longer written answers, true/false)

In this section, a multiple choice of mostly

single word answers is used to assess children's understanding of an information text and their abilities to re-organise the content to deduce information which is not directly stated.

When the child has read the first passage on page 19, explain that you want them to answer these questions by writing the answer, or by ticking true/false boxes as in Reading Test 2, or by drawing a ring round the word (or phrase) which best completes the sentence. Use the example question to show how this is done. Tell the child to stop at the end of page 24 (True/False).

**Spelling Test 1:** single words
The questions require children to show that they can correctly spell the words represented by the pictures.

Each word contains a common letter string and most of the words are simple and regular. Each word is cued by its initial letter. For all four Spelling Tests, the child should not be allowed to look back at earlier pages, as some of the words to be spelled are printed there. Show the child the example on page 25 (flag), and then help them to complete the practice question (tree).

You then have a choice of procedures.
*Either:*
a) Read out each word one at a time to the child. You may give an example of the word used in a sentence, although this is not necessary, as any ambiguity in the pictures (e.g. fire or flame) should be dispelled by the cued word.
*or*
b) Ask the child to complete all the other spellings down to the bottom of page 26 (question 10). If you follow this procedure, the child may write an acceptable alternative (flames instead of fire). You can tell the child that he or she may ask you for help if they are unsure about the precise word being cued by the picture.

**Spelling Test 2:** spelling and labelling
This activity tests the child's awareness and understanding of specific vocabulary used in the texts.

Use the example to show the child how to join each label to the appropriate part of the picture. If the child's first language is not English or they

are unfamiliar with this format, you may wish to go through this section very slowly, discussing each word, before asking the child to write in the spelling.

**Reading Test 4:** Castles
(non-fiction: multiple choice, written answers, true/false)

Ask the child to read the passage about *Castles*, and to answer the questions on it.

**Reading Test 5:** Time slip
(poem: written answers)

The questions on the poem test children's understanding of the poem's narrative and their ability to extract specific statements and events from the text. Tell the child to read the whole poem, and then to answer the questions on page 37. Use the example question to show the child how to do this.

**Spelling Test 3:** single words
Remind the child about the procedure using the example question on page 38. Ask the child to complete the spelling test in the same way as Spelling Test 1.

**Spelling Test 4:** Dictation
The text, which you read aloud, is printed on page 44 where you will find full instructions. This page can be photocopied or cut out to be used separately.

**Handwriting Test**
The Handwriting Test includes full instructions. Marking guidance is given on page 47.

## Marking the tests

A guide to marking is given on pages 45 to 48. Use the score boxes and page totals in each page margin to work out the child's score for each test. Then, transfer them to the test total boxes on page 48.

## Finding the National Curriculum Level

Complete the chart on page 48 when tests have been completed for a guide to the child's National Curriculum Levels in Reading and Spelling.

**Reading Test 1: Fiction**

Time started ⬚ : ⬚
Time finished ⬚ : ⬚

# THE GIANT BABY

There once was a giant who lived in Ireland.

His name was Finn and though he was big and strong, he was kind and gentle.

Oonagh, Finn's wife, thought he was also lazy.

**Ring the word that *best* answers each question:**

*Example:* What was the giant called?

Oonagh    (Finn)    Baby    Flynn

**1** Write the answer:

Which country did Finn live in?

 ------------------------------------------------------------

PAGE TOTAL

'Look at that fire, Finn,' said Oonagh. 'It's smoking. It always does that when the wind blows. Can't you do something about it?'

'Yes,' said Finn, 'I'll look at it.'

'Good,' said Oonagh. 'And when you have done that, you can go down to the spring and fetch me some water.'

'The thing is,' said Finn, 'I've got a bit of a problem. I'm trying to think of something I can do about it. Can't I get the water later?'

'Tell me your problem,' said Oonagh. 'I do the thinking in this house.'

**2** **What did the wind make the fire do?**

go out     smoke     grow bigger     grow smaller

☐

**3** **What did Oonagh want Finn to get from the spring?**

☐

PAGE TOTAL

'Well,' said Finn, 'there's another giant in town. He's twice as big as me and twice as strong. He wants to fight me, to show me who's boss.'

'I'll sort him out,' said Oonagh. 'I'll show him who's boss!' Oonagh fetched a cradle down from the attic.

Then she dressed Finn up as a baby.

'Get in the cradle, Finn,' she said.

'I can hardly fit into this,' grumbled Finn.

'I know,' said Oonagh. 'That's part of my plan.'

**4** What was Finn worried about?

| the other giant | fetching water |
| the fire | the cradle |

**5** Where did Oonagh get the cradle from?

a friend    her bedroom    her attic    Mothercare

PAGE TOTAL

Oonagh tucked Finn in and put some teddies in the cradle.
Then she went to the oven and baked six buns.

But these were no ordinary buns.

Each bun was as big as a sheep. Into five of the buns Oonagh
baked pots, pans, pebbles and stones. Into one bun she mixed
raisins and honey.

When the buns came out of the oven they all looked the same.
Then Oonagh iced the buns and put them
on a plate.

6    **What did Oonagh put in the cradle with Finn?**

✎ ------------------------------------------------------

7    **How many buns did Oonagh bake?**

✎ ------------------------------------------------------

8    **What did Oonagh put on all the buns?**

icing        sheep        stones        honey

PAGE
TOTAL

Oonagh had just finished the buns when there was a great thump on the door. It was the other giant, looking for Finn.

'Finn is not at home at the moment,' said Oonagh, 'but you can come in and wait for him.'

'He's just cutting down a couple of forests', she added, 'so he won't be very long.'

The new giant looked worried when he heard about the forests.

9   Who was at the door?

 ................................................................................

10   What did Oonagh say Finn was doing?

thumping the door        fetching water

cutting down forests        sleeping

'While you're waiting, can you turn the house round for me?' said Oonagh. 'It stops the fire smoking.'

The house was very heavy. The giant puffed as he struggled to move it.

'I hope that wasn't too difficult for you,' said Oonagh. 'Finn often does it, but he's much bigger than you.'

The giant looked even more worried.

**11** What did the giant turn round?

✎ ------------------------------------------------------------------------

**12** Why did the giant puff and struggle?

|  |  |
| --- | --- |
| he was old | he was unfit |
| the house was heavy | he was running |

'Can you do another job for me?' said Oonagh. 'There's a spring running under that mountain. If you could just move it a mile or two to the left, I could get my water from it.'

It took the giant a long time to move the mountain. He was worn out by the time he'd finished.

'Thank you,' said Oonagh. 'Now I'll make you a nice cup of tea, and you can have some of Finn's favourite buns.'

13  Where was the spring?

on a mountain                    under a mountain

in a forest                          by a tree

☐

14  What did the giant move?

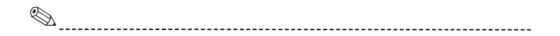

☐

PAGE
TOTAL

Oonagh gave the giant one of the huge buns. He bit into it greedily and cracked his teeth on the stones inside it.

He let out a yell. Finn yelled too. He was sure the giant was going to find him.

'Oh dear,' said Oonagh. 'You've woken the baby. I'd better give him a bun to keep him quiet.'

She gave Finn the bun with no stones in it and he gobbled it up.

The giant went over to the cradle and looked at Finn.

'Your baby is huge!' yelled the giant. 'That bun nearly broke my jaw. What can his teeth be like?''

He's only a baby,' said Oonagh. 'He hasn't got any teeth yet. See for yourself.'

**15** What did Oonagh give the giant?

✎ --------------------------------------------------------------

**16** What did the giant crack his teeth on?

a cup of tea          a sandwich

stones in the bun          an apple

**17** What did Oonagh give Finn?

a bun with stones in          some milk

a sweet          a bun with no stones in

PAGE TOTAL

The giant put his finger in Finn's mouth.
Finn bit the finger as hard as he could.

The giant let out a terrible yell.

'If that's a baby, I'm not waiting to meet
his dad!' shouted the giant, as he ran
out of the door.

'That showed him who's boss,'
laughed Finn.

'Yes,' said Oonagh, 'and I hope
it showed you too!'

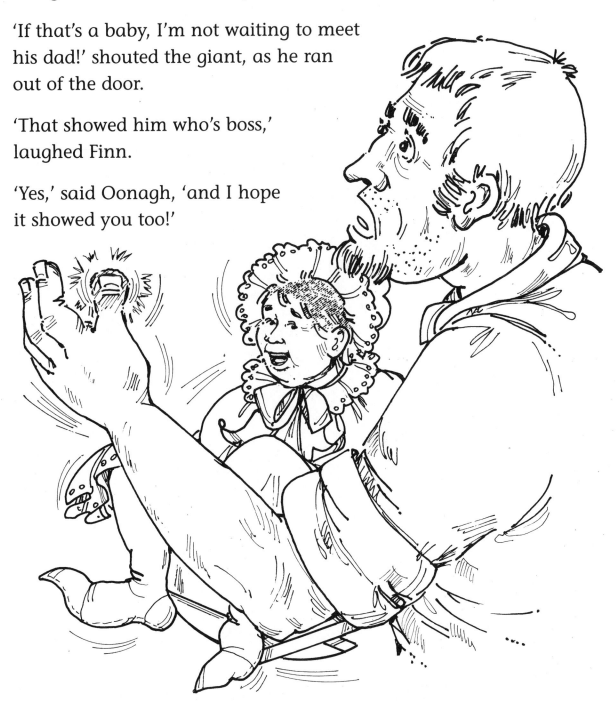

18 **Who turned out to be the real boss in this story?**

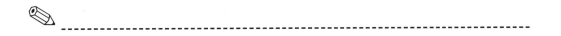

**• Reading Test 2: Non-Fiction •**

Time started | : |
Time finished | : |

# A real giant?

What do you think is the largest animal that has ever lived on Earth?

An elephant perhaps? Or one of the dinosaurs?

In fact the world's largest animal lives in the sea. It is the blue whale, which can be over 30 metres long – that is longer than two lorries.

| True or false? | True | False |
|---|---|---|
| *Example:* The largest animal is a dinosaur. | ☐ | ✔ |
| **1** A blue whale is bigger than the biggest dinosaur. | ☐ | ☐ |
| **2** A big lorry is the same length as a blue whale. | ☐ | ☐ |

PAGE TOTAL

A blue whale can weigh more than 150 tonnes — that is heavier than 30 elephants.

You may think the blue whale must eat great big fish, but in fact it eats only tiny creatures like shrimps which are called *krill*.

|  |  | True | False |  |
|---|---|---|---|---|
| 3 | A blue whale can weigh more than thirty elephants. | ☐ | ☐ | ☐ |
| 4 | Blue whales must eat great big fish. | ☐ | ☐ | ☐ |

PAGE TOTAL

During the last hundred years almost half a million blue whales have been killed for their meat and oil.

These pictures show whale hunting over seventy years ago.

A HARPOON-GUN.

THE HARPOONER.

Fewer than ten thousand of these real life giants are alive today.

The blue whale is now a protected species. This means that nobody is allowed to kill it.

|  |  | True | False |  |
|---|---|---|---|---|
| 5 | Blue whales were killed for their teeth and their fur. | ☐ | ☐ | ☐ |
| 6 | We have to kill whales to protect other species. | ☐ | ☐ | ☐ |

PAGE TOTAL

**Reading Test 3: Non-Fiction & Fiction**

Time started : 

Time finished : 

# Stories about giants

Why do we tell stories about giants?

For as long as people have been telling stories, they have been telling stories about giants. Some giant stories were made up to explain things nobody could understand.

In the next four pages you can read about three things which people once believed were made by giants.

This is a picture of the Giant's Causeway in Ireland.

The strange rocks look as if they have been shaped by gigantic tools.

People thought that giants had done the work.

---

**Choose the right word to fit the sentence.**

*Example:* The Giant's Causeway is near the

river        town        (sea)        sky

**1**   The Giant's Causeway is in

England        Ireland        Scotland        Wales        ☐

---

PAGE TOTAL

This is a circle of stones called Stonehenge. Nobody knows exactly why it was built.

It has been there for many hundreds of years.

It must have taken hundreds of people to move such heavy stones. People used to think that this stone circle could only have been made by giants.

2   Stonehenge is a stone

castle        square        circle        wall        ☐

3   Stonehenge was built by

circles        stone        giants        people        ☐

PAGE
TOTAL

This is Silbury Hill in Wiltshire. It was made by the people who lived in this part of England.

Nobody knows why it was built, so people made up stories to explain why it is there.

One of these stories tells how a giant was carrying a hill on his back. He was going to drop it on the town of Marlborough in Wiltshire, because the people who lived there had angered him.

4   Where was the giant going to drop the hill?

✎ --------------------------------------------------------------------------------

5   The people in the town had made the giant

angry        shoes        happy        tired

On the way he met a cobbler who was carrying lots of pairs of worn out shoes to mend.

The giant told the cobbler what he was going to do and asked him how far it was to Marlborough.

'Miles and miles and miles,' said the cobbler. 'I've just come from there myself and I've worn out all these shoes on the journey.'

**6** What was the cobbler carrying?

✎

**7** The cobbler told the giant that Marlborough was

just round the corner        a long way away

a mile away        three miles away

PAGE
TOTAL

'I can't be bothered to go all that way!' groaned the giant.

He dropped the hill and went home.

And that's why Silbury Hill is where it is today and not in the middle of the town of Marlborough! At least that's what the story says.

**8** **What sort of story do you think this is?**

A true story        History        A legend        A poem

PAGE
TOTAL

## True or false?

Here are some questions about what is true and what is false.

Tick the right box. Find the answers in the words and pictures on pages 19 to 23.

|  |  | True | False |
|---|---|---|---|
| *Example:* The rocks on the Giant's Causeway were cut by giants. | | ☐ | ✔ |
| **9** Stonehenge is many hundreds of years old. | | ☐ | ☐ |
| **10** Some of the stones are on top of other stones at Stonehenge. | | ☐ | ☐ |
| **11** Silbury Hill is in Ireland. | | ☐ | ☐ |
| **12** Silbury Hill was built for children to roll down it. | | ☐ | ☐ |

PAGE TOTAL

• Spelling Test 1 •

Time started ⠀⠀:

Time finished ⠀⠀:

# Spelling

Write the word underneath each picture.
Try to spell each word correctly.

*Example:*

f<u>lag</u>

*Practice:*

t_____

**1**

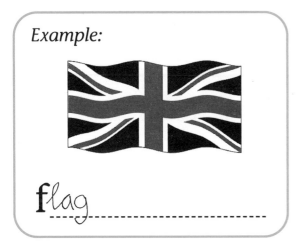

c_____

**2**

c_____

**3**

d_____

**4**

c_____

PAGE TOTAL

Write the word underneath each picture.
Try to spell each word correctly.

**5**

w_____

**6**

h_____

**7**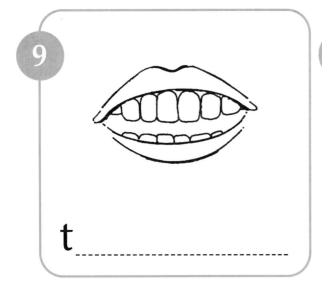

f_____

**8**

m_____

**9**

t_____

**10**

f_____

PAGE TOTAL

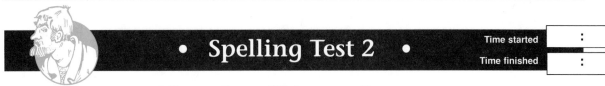

• Spelling Test 2 •

Time started   :

Time finished   :

# The Spelling Game

Write the words in the boxes:

**Example**

tree

n ₁

h ₂

h ₃

r ₄

s ₅

p ₆

b ₇

b ₈

s ₉

PAGE TOTAL

**• Reading Test 4: Non-Fiction •**

Time started  :

Time finished  :

# CASTLES

The first British castles were hill forts. They were built by the Celts, who lived in Britain over two thousand years ago.

A tribe used to build its village on top of a hill and dig deep ditches around it, to protect the village from their enemies.

The ditches were so huge that they can still be seen today.

---

***Example:*** The first British castles were built by the

Romans        Normans        (Celts)        French

**1**  We know where the Celts built forts because today we can still see the

 --------------------------------------------------

PAGE
TOTAL

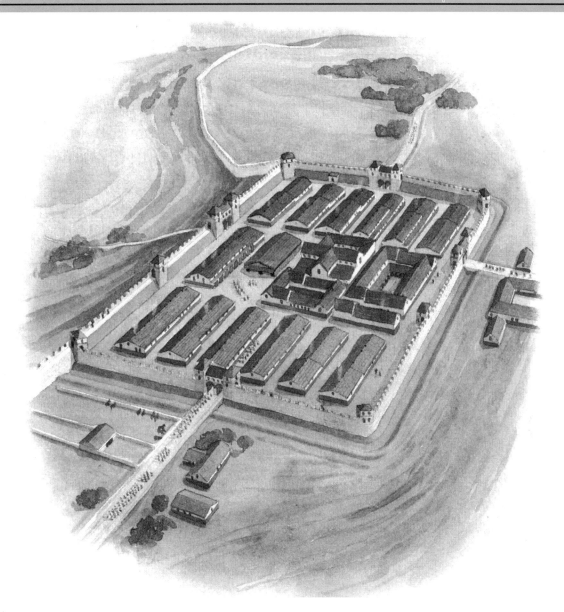

Two thousand years ago Britain was invaded by people called the Romans. Their huge army forts were built by Roman soldiers, who made strong walls as well as ditches.

**2** The next people who invaded Britain after the Celts were the

✎ ------------------------------------------------------------

**3** Roman forts were built by

✎ ------------------------------------------------------------

PAGE TOTAL

About a thousand years ago Britain was invaded by the Normans, who came from Northern France. They built a type of castle called a Motte and Bailey.

A strong wooden tower was put up on top of a huge mound. This was the **Motte**. It was used as a look-out tower to spot the enemy.

The **Bailey** was an area protected by wooden walls and ditches. This is where people lived, stored their food, and kept their animals.

4  The _____ was an area below the Motte. ☐

5  Most people and their animals lived inside the

✎ _____ ☐

When the Normans had conquered Britain they began to build castles of stone, which were much stronger than wooden castles. Look at this picture of a castle. It is more like a small town than a home.

It is surrounded by a ditch or moat filled with water. The only way into this castle is across the drawbridge.

If a castle was attacked by an enemy army the people inside would need enough food and water to last several weeks.

6 ✎ _____ castles were stronger than wooden ones.

7 ✎ _____ were dug around castles and filled with water.

8 Norman stone castles could resist an attack for

✎ _____

There were many ways of attacking a castle.

Some castles were so strong that an enemy had to camp outside the walls and wait for the people inside to run out of food and water. This was called a **siege**.

People stopped building castles when gunpowder was invented. Even the strongest walls could be knocked down by big guns.

**9**   During a siege, you waited for the people inside the castle to run out of food and

✎ _____

**10**   Even stone castles could not resist

✎ _____

PAGE TOTAL

**True or false?** Tick the right box. Read pages 28 to 32 to find the answers.

|  | True | False |
|---|:---:|:---:|
| ***Example:*** This castle was built by the Romans. | ☐ | ✔ |

**11** The first British castles were hill forts. ☐ ☐

**12** The Romans lived in Britain before the Celts. ☐ ☐

**13** The Normans came from the North of England. ☐ ☐

**14** The Normans built drawbridges across moats. ☐ ☐

**15** Cows and horses were kept inside the Bailey. ☐ ☐

**16** The Normans built both wooden and stone castles. ☐ ☐

**17** A moat is a kind of stone wall. ☐ ☐

**18** The invention of gunpowder helped to end the building of castles. ☐ ☐

PAGE TOTAL

• **Reading Test 5: Poetry** •

| Time started | : |
| Time finished | : |

Read the poem called 'Time slip', then answer the questions on page 37.

# Time slip

I was playing with my brother

On the Cleadon Castle Hill,

When we heard a ghostly howling.

We both stood very still.


The sun had disappeared,

The mist swirled round our feet.

I looked up at the ruins.

The Castle stood complete!


We saw, high on the battlements,

An archer with his bow.

Suddenly he spotted us —

'Two enemies below!'

The drawbridge started lowering,

We turned and fled in fright.

The horse's hooves drew nearer.

The rider was a knight.


He pulled his horse before us.

'Stand fast, young sirs. Hold back!

Why spy on yonder castle?

Does your master plan attack?'


My brother and I stammered,

'We're playing Hide and Seek.

We don't know why this happened.'

We both could hardly speak.

'All lies!' The knight was angry.

'Kneel down. I'll stop your tears!'

We hid our eyes and trembled.

His sword flashed past our ears.


It seemed like hours later,

I lifted up my head.

The castle was in ruins.

'He's gone,' my brother said.


'Look,' I shook my brother,

'It must have been a dream.'

Maybe, but all around us

The hoofprints could be seen!


*Wendy Larmont*

## Time slip

Here are some questions about the poem *Time slip*.
You only need to write one word for each answer.

*Example:* What was on top of the hill my brother and I were playing on?          *Ruins*

**1** What noise did we hear?

**2** What swirled round our feet?

**3** Who saw us from the castle?

**4** Which part of the castle came down?

**5** What did the knight think the boy and his brother were doing?

**6** What did the knight order them to do?

**7** What flashed past their ears?

**8** What made the boy think it might not have been a dream?

**9** What do you think the knight was?

**10** What would you feel if this had happened to you?

## • Spelling Test 3 •

| Time started | : |
| Time finished | : |

*Example:*

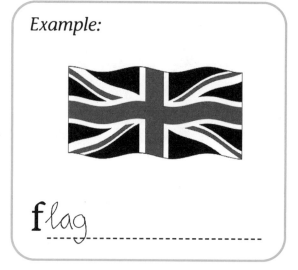

f*lag* _____

**1**

h _____

Write the word underneath
each picture.
Try to spell each word correctly.

**2**

b _____

**3**

d _____

PAGE
TOTAL

Write the word underneath each picture.
Try to spell each word correctly.

**4**

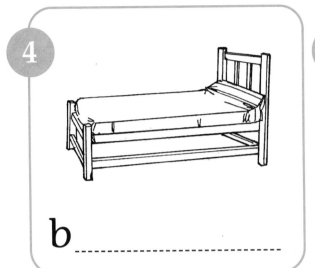

b _____

**5**

t _____

**6**

b _____

**7**

f _____

**8**

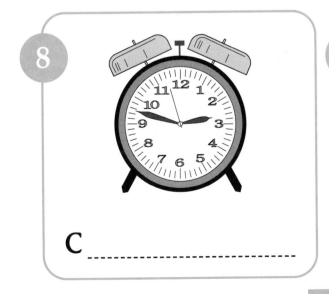

c _____

**9**

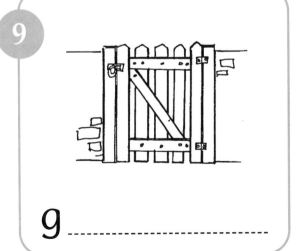

g _____

PAGE TOTAL

Write the word underneath each picture.
Try to spell each word correctly.

**10**

s _____

**11**

h _____

**12**

d _____

**13**

t _____

**14**

k _____

**15**
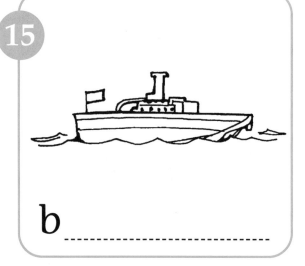
b _____

PAGE
TOTAL

• **Spelling Test 4: Dictation** •

Time started : 

Time finished : 

# Castles Dictation

Write the missing words on the dotted lines.
Try to spell each word correctly.

You can ..._still_... see many different castles ..................... ₁ .

Some castles are still used and lived in, like the ................... ₂ of London. People have lived in it ever since the ................. ₃ part was ............................ ₄ in 1038. It has been used as royal palace, a ..................... ₅ and at one time it was used as a ................... ₆ ! Many people ..................... ₇ it now to look at the crown ................... ₈ which are kept there.

The ..................... ₉ castles were put up by the Celts. They were wooden and ................... ₁₀ of them .........................., ₁₁ but we can still see the ................. ₁₂ ditches they dug ........................ ₁₃ them.

When the Normans ........................ ₁₄ Britain they also cut down trees to make castles very ........................ ₁₅ . Most of these ..................... ₁₆ castles were replaced by stone castles. Stone castles took much .................. ₁₇ time to put up, but they were much ........................... ₁₈ .

PAGE TOTAL

One of the most .......................... <sub>19</sub> stone castles was

Pontefract Castle, in Yorkshire. There was ........................ <sub>20</sub>

an old fort on the .................... <sub>21</sub> when the Normans

........................ <sub>22</sub> it. They .......................... <sub>23</sub> a new round

castle made of stone.


Over the next five .......................... <sub>24</sub> , Pontefract Castle

grew in size until it was the .......................... <sub>25</sub> castle in

England. In 1649, during the English Civil War, the

........................ <sub>26</sub> in the castle .............................. <sub>27</sub> after a

long ................. <sub>28</sub> .


Although it had taken hundreds of years to ................... <sub>29</sub> ,

Pontefract Castle was .......................... <sub>30</sub> in about ten

weeks.

• **Handwriting Test** •

*The ruined keep of Pontefract Castle, 1827*

# Handwriting

Copy these three sentences in your best handwriting:

Today, all that is left of Pontefract Castle
is a few bits of wall and two underground
rooms. The only entrance to one of the
rooms is through a hole in the ceiling.
It was probably a dark and damp dungeon.

--------------------------------------------------------

--------------------------------------------------------

--------------------------------------------------------

--------------------------------------------------------

--------------------------------------------------------

PAGE
TOTAL

# • Spelling Test 4: Dictation •

First ask the child to turn to page 41, where they will find the passage below with missing words.

Then read out the whole of the passage below. Say that you are going to read the passage again more slowly, so that they can fill in the missing words (the 'target' words, printed in bold type). Tell the child to write the missing words on the dotted lines and to try to spell each word correctly. Use the first word in bold type (**still**) as an example.

Continue reading the passage, pausing at each target word. Repeat the target word and allow the child sufficient time to write the word in the dotted line space provided. Target words should be repeated only once. Each target word space is numbered, from 1 to 30, to assist in marking.

The test is constructed so that you may finish the test at the end of any of the six paragraphs, if it is clearly too difficult.

---

You can **still** see many different castles **today**$_1$.

Some castles are still used and lived in, like the **Tower**$_2$ of London. People have lived in it ever since the **first**$_3$ part was **finished**$_4$ in 1038. It has been used as royal palace, a **prison**$_5$ and at one time it was used as a **zoo**$_6$! Many people **visit**$_7$ it now to look at the crown **jewels**$_8$ which are kept there.

The **earliest**$_9$ castles were put up by the Celts. They were wooden and **none**$_{10}$ of them **survives**$_{11}$, but we can still see the **huge**$_{12}$ ditches they dug **around**$_{13}$ them.

When the Normans **invaded**$_{14}$ Britain they also cut down trees to make castles very **quickly**$_{15}$. Most of these **simple**$_{16}$ castles were replaced by stone castles. Stone castles took much **more**$_{17}$ time to put up, but they were much **stronger**$_{18}$.

One of the most **beautiful**$_{19}$ stone castles was Pontefract Castle, in Yorkshire. There was **already**$_{20}$ an old fort on the **site**$_{21}$ when the Normans **occupied**$_{22}$ it. They **constructed**$_{23}$ a new round castle made of stone.

Over the next five **centuries**$_{24}$, Pontefract Castle grew in size until it was the **largest**$_{25}$ castle in England. In 1649, during the English Civil War, the **soldiers**$_{26}$ in the castle **surrendered**$_{27}$ after a long **siege**$_{28}$.

Although it had taken hundreds of years to **build**$_{29}$, Pontefract Castle was **demolished**$_{30}$ in about ten weeks.

# • Answers: Reading •

## Marking Guide

Where the question has a multiple choice of answers, only the correct answer is acceptable, but where the child is required to write an answer in one or more words, a variety of possible answers may be given. Likely alternative answers are given in brackets, but you may use your judgement to decide if an answer is acceptable.

### Reading Test 1: Pages 7–15

The giant baby
*Example:* Finn
1. Ireland
2. smoke
3. water
4. the other giant
5. her attic
6. teddies (some teddies / teddy)
7. six
8. icing (icing sugar)
9. the other giant (the new giant / another giant)
10. cutting down forests
11. house (the house / Finn's house / Oonagh's house)
12. the house was heavy
13. under a mountain
14. a mountain
15. a bun (bun with stones in)
16. stones in the bun
17. a bun with no stones in
18. Oonagh

### Reading Test 2: Pages 16–18

A real giant?
*Example:* False ✓
1. True
2. False
3. True
4. False
5. False
6. False

### Reading Test 3: Pages 19–23

Stories about giants
*Example:* sea
1. Ireland
2. circle
3. people
4. Marlborough
5. angry
6. shoes (worn out shoes)
7. a long way away
8. A legend

### Page 24 True / False

*Example:* False ✓
9. True
10. True
11. False
12. False

### Reading Test 4: Pages 28–32

Castles
*Example:* Celts
1. ditches
2. Romans (Roman soldiers)
3. soldiers (Roman soldiers)
4. Bailey
5. Bailey
6. Stone
7. Moats
8. weeks (several weeks)
9. water
10. guns (gunpowder)

### Page 33 True / False

*Example:* False ✓
11. True
12. False
13. False
14. True
15. True
16. True
17. False
18. True

### Reading Test 5: Page 37

Time slip
*Example:* Ruins
1. howling
2. mist
3. archer
4. drawbridge
5. spying
6. kneel
7. sword
8. hoofprints
9. ghost / vision / dream
10. fear / awe / confusion / puzzlement

# • Answers: Spelling •

## Spelling Test 1: Pages 25–26

*Example:* flag
*Practice:* tree
1. cat
2. cow
3. dog
4. car
5. wall
6. house
7. fire (flames)
8. mice
9. teeth
10. flowers

## Spelling Test 2: Page 27

The Spelling Game
*Example:* tree
1. nose
2. hand
3. hill
4. rope
5. shoe(s)
6. patch
7. boot
8. bag
9. stick

## Spelling Test 3: Pages 38–40

*Example:* flag

1. hat
2. bus
3. doll
4. bed
5. toys
6. book
7. frog
8. clock
9. gate
10. swan
11. horse
12. dragon
13. trumpet
14. knife
15. boat

## Spelling Test 4: Dictation: Page 41

*Example:* still
1. today
2. Tower
3. first
4. finished
5. prison
6. zoo
7. visit
8. jewels
9. earliest
10. none
11. survives
12. huge
13. around
14. invaded
15. quickly
16. simple
17. more
18. stronger
19. beautiful
20. already
21. site
22. occupied
23. constructed
24. centuries
25. largest
26. soldiers
27. surrendered
28. siege
29. build
30. demolished

# • Handwriting Test •

The examples below should help you to get a good idea about the National Curriculum level of a child's handwriting.

➠ *Look at the example for Level 1. If a child's writing is better than this, but not as good as the example for Level 3, then the child's handwriting will be at Level 2, the level for most children at the end of Key Stage 1.*

➠ *If a child's writing is better than the example for Level 3, but not as good as the example for Level 5, then it will be at Level 4.*

The written descriptions below are a summary of the National Curriculum Guidelines – these may be helpful if children have learned a different style from those in the examples. The particular handwriting style children use is not a factor which is considered. What is important is the quality of the handwriting, whatever style it is in.

**Level 1 example**

> woter boheobob.
> A church was built on the
> pluce where he bieb.

**Level 3 example**

> On the 17th March it was st patnick
> day. He was borned in wales. his father
> was a Roman. A.D. 389 - A.D. 461. st Patnick
> was on the beach.

**Level 5 example**

> On Sheilas birthday her daddy gave
> her a very unusual present he took her
> out into the garden and gave her a

**Level 6 example**

> Autumn is one of the most interesting seasons for
> trees. They often change colour and suffer from the loss
> of leaves. The buds begin to appear, and one can

| National Curriculum Level 1: |
|---|
| Some recognisable letters. |

| National Curriculum Level 2: |
|---|
| Letters generally formed correctly, with upper case (e.g. ABCDE) or lower case (e.g. abcde) letters used consistently. |

| National Curriculum Level 3: |
|---|
| Beginnings of clear legible writing, showing some ability to join letters. |

| National Curriculum Level 4: |
|---|
| More fluent writing which is legible / mostly joined letters / regular spacing and size. |

| National Curriculum Level 5: |
|---|
| Clear, legible, neat in a cursive style. |

| National Curriculum Level 6: |
|---|
| Mature, clear, legible, neat in a cursive style. |

## READING
Write each test score below.

TEST 1 – FICTION ☐ /18

TEST 2 – NON-FICTION ☐ /6

TEST 3 – NON-FICTION & FICTION ☐ /12

TEST 4 – NON-FICTION ☐ /18

TEST 5 – POETRY ☐ /10

**TOTAL READING SCORE** ☐ /64

## SPELLING
Write each test score below.

TEST 1 ☐ /10

TEST 2 ☐ /9

TEST 3 ☐ /15

TEST 4 – DICTATION ☐ /30

**TOTAL SPELLING SCORE** ☐ /64

### Finding National Curriculum Levels in Reading and Spelling

Work out the child's scores for Reading and for Spelling; write them in the boxes above, and total them.

Ring the total scores achieved in Reading and Spelling on the central Score Scale.

Then, read across from each to find the National Curriculum Levels – to the left for Reading; to the right for Spelling.

| READING LEVELS | SCORE SCALE | SPELLING LEVELS |
|---|---|---|
| Upper Level 4 | 64 | LEVEL 4 |
|  | 63 | or above |
|  | 62 |  |
|  | 61 |  |
|  | 60 |  |
|  | 59 |  |
| LEVEL 4 | 58 |  |
|  | 57 |  |
|  | 56 |  |
|  | 55 |  |
|  | 54 |  |
|  | 53 |  |
|  | 52 |  |
|  | 51 |  |
| Lower Level 4 | 50 | Lower Level 4 |
|  | 49 |  |
| Upper Level 3 | 48 | Upper Level 3 |
|  | 47 |  |
|  | 46 |  |
|  | 45 |  |
|  | 44 |  |
|  | 43 |  |
|  | 42 |  |
|  | 41 |  |
|  | 40 |  |
| LEVEL 3 | 39 | LEVEL 3 |
|  | 38 |  |
|  | 37 |  |
|  | 36 |  |
|  | 35 |  |
|  | 34 |  |
| Lower Level 3 | 33 |  |
|  | 32 |  |
|  | 31 |  |
| Upper Level 2 | 30 |  |
|  | 29 | Lower Level 3 |
|  | 28 |  |
|  | 27 |  |
|  | 26 | Upper Level 2 |
|  | 25 |  |
|  | 24 |  |
|  | 23 |  |
|  | 22 |  |
| LEVEL 2 | 21 |  |
|  | 20 |  |
|  | 19 |  |
|  | 18 |  |
|  | 17 |  |
|  | 16 | LEVEL 2 |
|  | 15 |  |
|  | 14 |  |
|  | 13 |  |
| Lower Level 2 | 12 |  |
|  | 11 |  |
|  | 10 |  |
|  | 9 |  |
|  | 8 | Lower Level 2 |
|  | 7 |  |
| Working towards Level 2 | 6 |  |
|  | 5 | Working towards Level 2 |
|  | 4 |  |
|  | 3 |  |
|  | 2 |  |
|  | 1 |  |